ON A CAR JOURNEY

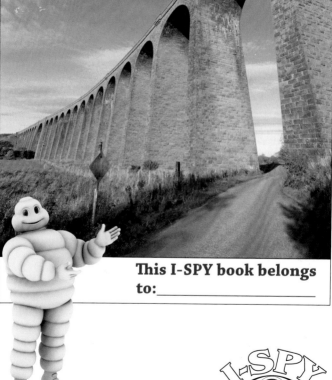

This I-SPY book belongs to: ______________________

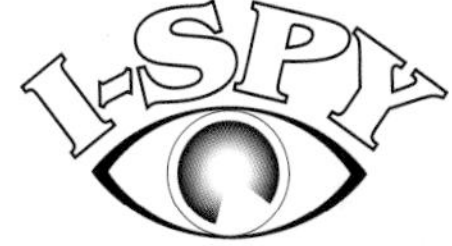

Introduction

If you take I-Spy On a Car Journey with you, every trip, no matter how long or short, will be fun for you and the family. And, you'll have a record of everything you'll have seen and you can compare notes with your friends when you get back.

If the journey is to be a long one, say, from one side of the country to the other, it's worth taking the time and trouble to do a bit of planning.

Look at a road atlas and follow the route that you're going to take, and, when you're travelling, you can make sure you'll know which road you're on and exactly where you are. Try to estimate how long you think the journey might take, bearing in mind the distance and the average speed you think the driver might take.

If you keep your eyes open and keep looking all around you, there's so much to see on a car journey. It's fun to find out about the world as it rushes by and you'll be surprised by all the fascinating things you'll discover. But, whatever you do, do not distract the driver by pointing things out to him or her. And, be sure to wear seatbelts and make yourself as comfortable as possible.

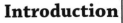

How to use your I-SPY book

There are so many things you could look out for on a car journey that it's hard to know where to begin, what to include, or what to leave out. Your I-Spy On a Car Journey book aims to give you some ideas but, once you've spotted everything here, why not come up with some more ideas of your own? You need 1000 points to send off for your I-Spy certificate (see page 64) but that is not too difficult because there are masses of points in every book. As you make each I-Spy, write your score in the box.

Road Building and Repair

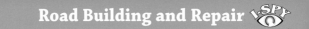

If you see these signs, you might be in for a short delay, so look out for some of the excavators and loaders on the next page.

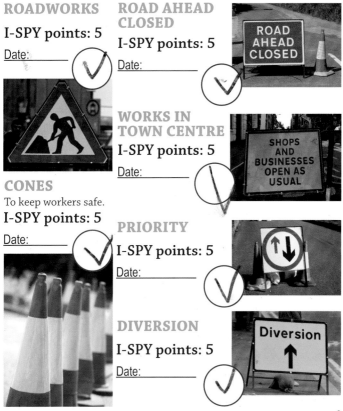

ROADWORKS

I-SPY points: 5

Date: ____________

CONES

To keep workers safe.

I-SPY points: 5

Date: ____________

ROAD AHEAD CLOSED

I-SPY points: 5

Date: ____________

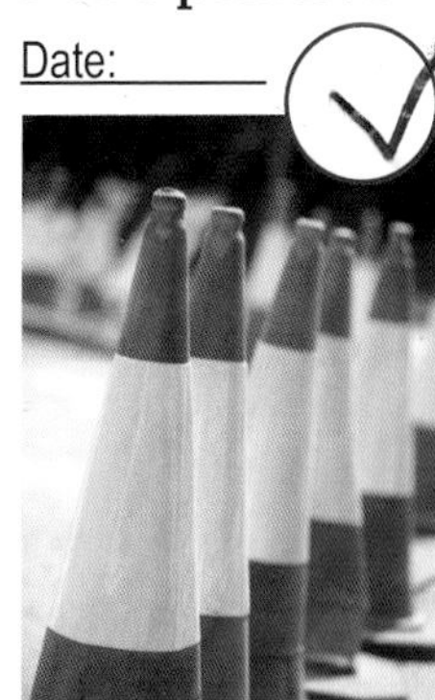

WORKS IN TOWN CENTRE

I-SPY points: 5

Date: ____________

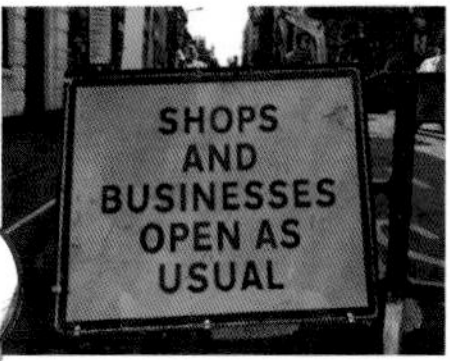

PRIORITY

I-SPY points: 5

Date: ____________

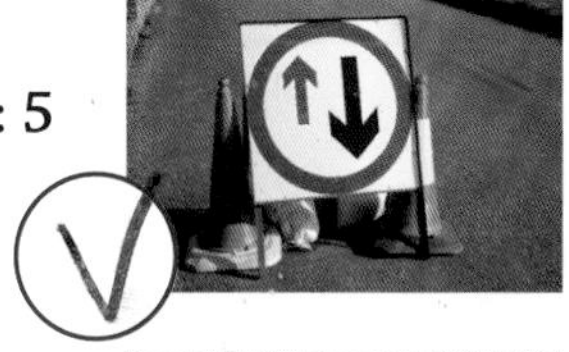

DIVERSION

I-SPY points: 5

Date: ____________

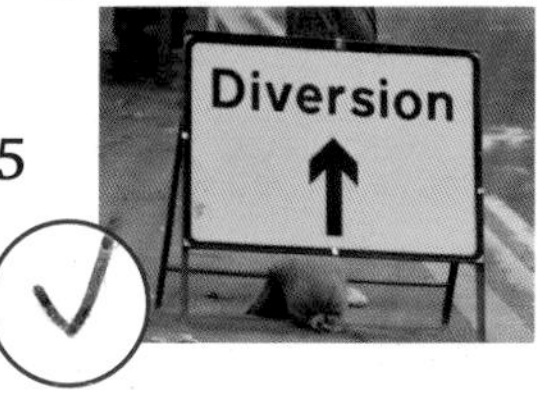

Road Building and Repair

Excavators and rollers rake and flatten to earth to make a smooth surface for a new road.

DIGGING UP THE ROAD

I-SPY points: 5 for each type of vehicle

Date:

LAYING TARMAC

Then tarmac can be spread to make a hard durable road surface.

I-SPY points: 5

Date:

TRACKED EXCAVATOR

I-SPY points: 5

Date:

WHEEL LOADER

This one has a big bucket on the front.

I-SPY points: 5

Date:

BACKHOE LOADER

Note the scoop mounted at the rear.

I-SPY points: 5

Date:

TRACKED EXCAVATOR WITH SCOOP

I-SPY points: 5

Date:

The Law in Action

Throughout the country the police will be there, seven days a week and 24 hours a day, to enforce the law or to offer help and advice.

BLUE LAMP

Traditionally, the sign of the police station.

I-SPY points: 10

Date:

POLICE BOX

Once a common sight on British streets. It is now more common as Dr Who's Tardis!

I-SPY points: 25

Date:

WHEEL CLAMP

Oh dear! This driver will come back to a nasty surprise when they return to their vehicle.

I-SPY points: 5

Date:

Driving too fast can be dangerous. These devices help police to measure the speed of passing cars.

SPEED CAMERA

I-SPY points: 5

Date:

POLICE VAN WITH CAMERA

I-SPY points: 5

Date:

SPEED GUN

I-SPY points: 5

Date:

POLICE MOTORBIKE

I-SPY points: 5

Date:

POLICE VEHICLES

There are many types of police vehicles currently in use. Here is a selection.

I-SPY points: 5 for each of these

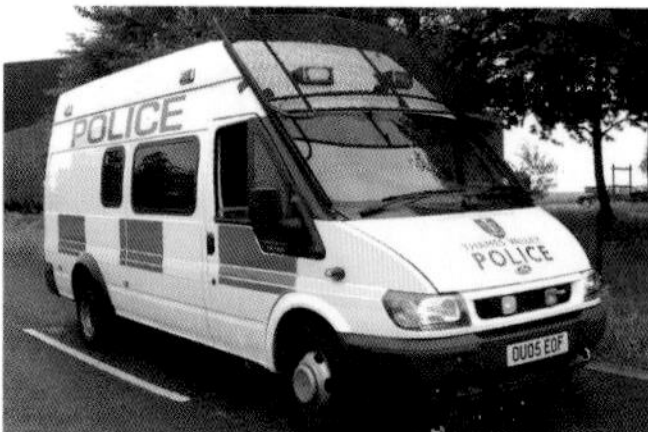

Date:

Date:

Date:

If your car breaks down, you might need a roadside recovery vehicle. Recovery trucks are heavy vehicles strong enough to transport smaller cars and trucks.

FIRE ENGINE

Fire Engines, like the police and ambulance services have blue flashing lights.

I-SPY points: 10

Date: ___________

RECOVERY TRUCK

I-SPY points: 5

Date: ___________

AA VAN

I-SPY points: 5 and 5 points for any other recovery service

Date: ___________

CRASH RECOVERY

I-SPY points: 10

Date: ___________

I-SPY Help at Hand

Ambulances have fluorescent strips and blue flasing lights so that they are highly visible on the road.

AMBULANCE

I-SPY points: 5

Date: __________

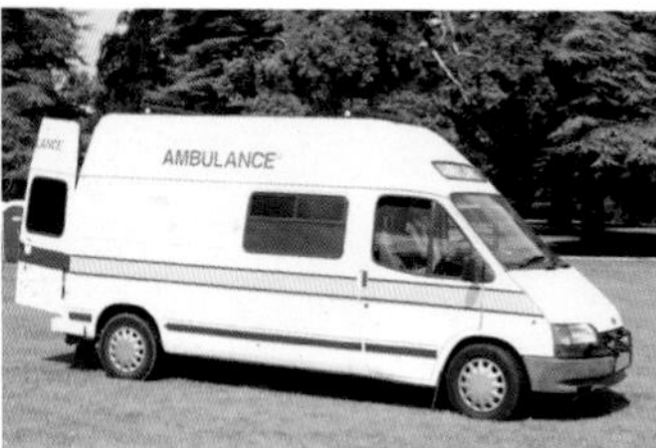

AMBULANCE

I-SPY points: 5

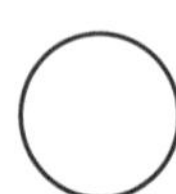

Date: __________

AMBULANCE HELICOPTER

The air ambulance helicopter can transport crash victims to hospital very quickly.

I-SPY points: 20

Date: __________

You'll find different post boxes in most towns and villages. They are often stamped with a date when the post box was put in place. Post boxes also have the royal cypher of the monarch on them.

TRADITIONAL RED POST BOX

I-SPY points: 5

Date: ___________

DOUBLE POST BOX

I-SPY points: 10

Date: ___________

SINGLE POST BOX

I-SPY points: 5

Date: ___________

POST OFFICE

I-SPY points: 5

Date: ____________

POST OFFICE SIGN

Post offices now have lozenge-shaped signs.

I-SPY points: 5

Date: ____________

RED PHONE BOX

Phone boxes are disappearing from our towns.

I-SPY points: 5

Date: ____________

BLUE PHONE BOX

I-SPY points: 25

Date: ____________

The Royal Mail transports many millions of letters every day. As well as delivering on foot, the small van is used for local collections, while the articulated lorry moves large quantities of post between cities.

POSTAL VANS

I-SPY points: 5
for each of these

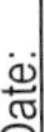

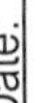

War memorials and statues are erected in honour of famous people and events.

STATUE OF QUEEN VICTORIA

I-SPY points: 10

Date:

WAR MEMORIAL

I-SPY points: 10

Date:

TOILET

I-SPY points: 5

Date: ____________

TOWN HALL

The Town Hall is usually centrally placed and may be quite a grand building.

I-SPY points: 5

Date: ____________

ALMS HOUSES

Traditional place for the elderly of the village to live.

I-SPY points: 15

Date: ____________

SKIP

Used to clear large quantities of waste.

I-SPY points: 15

Date: ____________

MARKET

The market brings hustle and bustle to the streets with vendors selling farmers' produce and homemade foods.

I-SPY points: 20

Date:

ORNAMENTAL FOUNTAIN

I-SPY points: 10

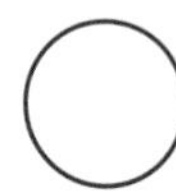

Date:

PADDLING POOL

Great for hot summer days!

I-SPY points: 20

Date:

CIRCUS

I-SPY points: 25

Date:

FLAGS

Can be found outside town halls and other public buildings.

I-SPY points: 10 for each flag, 5 points for other flags

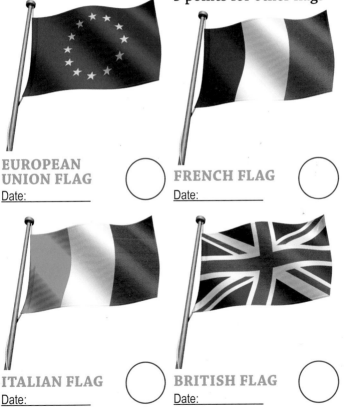

EUROPEAN UNION FLAG

Date: ____________

FRENCH FLAG

Date: ____________

ITALIAN FLAG

Date: ____________

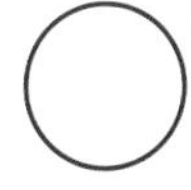

BRITISH FLAG

Date: ____________

VILLAGE FAIR

Village fairs are a lot of fun especially in the summer.

I-SPY points: 10

Date: ____________

PUB GARDEN

Pub gardens are a great place to relax on a fine day with a lemonade.

I-SPY points: 5

Date: ____________

DUCK POND

Be very careful of the water.

I-SPY points: 20

Date: ____________

ANCIENT MONUMENT

There are 1,000 stone circles like this in the British Isles.

I-SPY points: 10

Date:

CHALK MAN

The White Horse and the Cerne Abbas Giant are carved into chalky hillsides in southern England.

I-SPY points: 15

Date:

CHALK HORSE

I-SPY points: 15

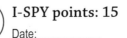

Date:

During the summer, the countryside is very colourful. Poppies are used for medicines, rape seed is harvested for its oil, and lavender is used by the perfume industry. See if you can smell the difference in the crops.

POPPY FIELD

I-SPY points: 15

Date: ____________

RAPE FIELD

I-SPY points: 15

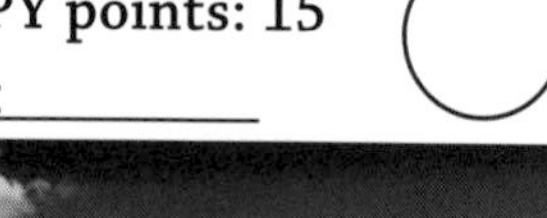

Date: ____________

LAVENDER FIELD

I-SPY points: 15

Date: ____________

There are many animals in our countryside – here are just a few.

COWS

I-SPY points: 5

Date:

DEER

I-SPY points: 20

Date:

SHEEP

I-SPY points: 5

Date:

PIGS

I-SPY points: 5

Double with piglets

Date:

HORSE

I-SPY points: 5

Date:

HIGHLAND CATTLE

I-SPY points: 20

Date:

CONVEX MIRROR

This convex mirror helps drivers see round corners on narrow roads by giving a wide angle.

I-SPY points: 20

Date:

BALES OF STRAW

Bales of straw fill the fields in May and June and change the appearance of the field.

I-SPY points: 10

Date:

TRACTOR

After the harvest, tractors plough the fields ready for the next crop.

I-SPY points: 10

Date:

COMBINE HARVESTER

Giant combine harvesters gather in wheat.

I-SPY points: 15

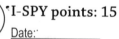

Date:

TRUCK WITH CRANE

Really heavy loads are carried on trucks with their own small cranes to lift goods on board.

I-SPY points: 20

Date: ____________

TRUCK TRAILER

Articulated lorries transport huge containers.

I-SPY points: 10

Date: ____________

FORK LIFT TRUCK

Fork lift trucks move pallets from warehouses to trucks quickly and easily.

I-SPY points: 10

Date: ____________

REFUSE COLLECTOR

Watch out for the bin lorry in your road!

I-SPY points: 10

Date: ____________

On the Road

COACHES

You might travel by coach on a long journey.

I-SPY points: 5

Date: ____________

TAXI CAB

Take a taxi ride in the city. Many taxis are black.

I-SPY points: 5

Date: ____________

TRADITIONAL RED DOUBLE DECKER BUS

Red routemaster buses are normally only seen in London.

I-SPY points: 20

Date: ____________

SINGLE DECKER BUS

Hop on a 'hopper' bus.

I-SPY points: 5

Date: ____________

DOUBLE DECKER BUS (NOT RED)

Double-decker buses have a great view from the top deck and are often used for tourist trips.

I-SPY points: 20

Date: ____________

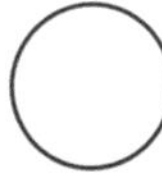

CAR WITH BIKES

Look out for cars carrying bikes on the roof...

I-SPY points: 10

Date: ____________

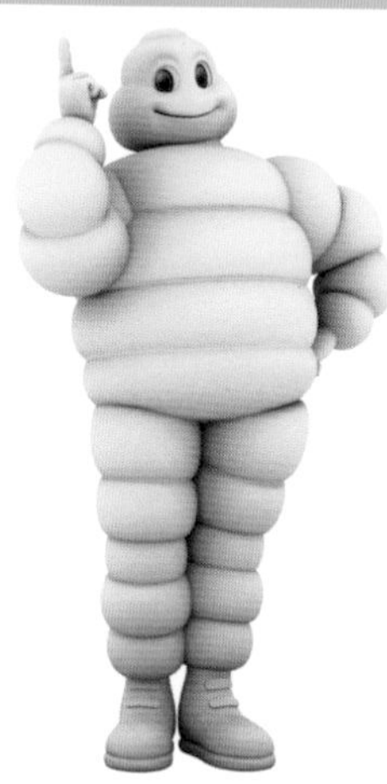

CAR WITH BOAT

...or even a canoe for the more adventurous!

I-SPY points: 5

Date: ____________

CAR WITH ROOF BOX

Roof-top boxes can store everything you need for a holiday.

I-SPY points: 5

Date: ____________

CYCLE COURIER

Cycle couriers are often quicker than courier vans in busy cities.

I-SPY points: 10

Date: ____________

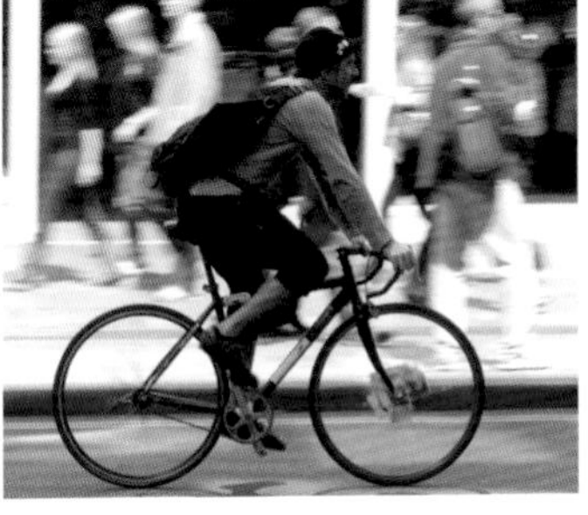

COURIER VAN

Delivering many small parcels every day.

I-SPY points: 5

Date: ____________

CARAVAN

Caravans and camper vans let you pack up and take your home wherever you like!

I-SPY points: 5

Date: ____________

CAMPER VAN

For ultimate mobility – with your own luxuries.

I-SPY points: 5

Date: ____________

MILK FLOAT

Milk floats are driven by electric motors in the cities.

I-SPY points: 5

Date: ____________

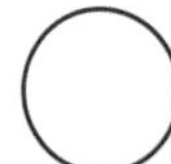

TRACTION ENGINE

Old steam-driven vehicles are often shown at fêtes – see if you can have a ride on one!

I-SPY points: 10

Date: ____________

STEAM ROLLER

I-SPY points: 10

Date: ____________

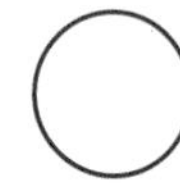

CAR TRANSPORTER

New cars appear to be perched on top of car transporters but are safely tied down.

I-SPY points: 5

Date:

VINTAGE TRUCK

Old vintage trucks are rounder and slower than modern ones.

I-SPY points: 5

Date:

SNACK VAN

The silver insulation on the snack van helps to keep the snacks hot.

I-SPY points: 5

Date:

ICECREAM VAN

Or you might prefer something a bit colder!

I-SPY points: 5

Date:

POWER STATION

Giant concrete cooling towers puff out clouds of steam from power stations.

I-SPY points: 15

Date: ____________

PYLONS

The electricity generated by the power station is carried across the country on high wires held up by steel pylons.

I-SPY points: 5

Date: ____________

WINDMILL

Windmills use the breeze to turn their sails.

I-SPY points: 15

Date: ____________

I-SPY points: Add 10 points for each different type of windmill spotted

WIND TURBINES

Wind turbines use the wind to generate electricity.

I-SPY points: 5

Date: ____________

WATERMILL

Look out for an old-fashioned water wheel turning water into power.

I-SPY points: 15

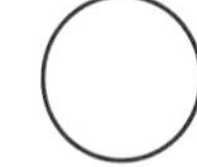

Date: ____________

FUN FAIR

No one can resist the fun of the fair!

I-SPY points: 25

Date:

MORRIS DANCING

A traditional style dating back hundreds of years, popular at village fêtes.

I-SPY points: 25

Date:

CRICKET

You may see a game being played on a village green especially on a summers day.

I-SPY points: 15

Date:

KITE FLYING

Take advantage of the sea breeze to fly a kite. Great fun!

I-SPY points: 20

Date: ____________

BOWLS

Bowls is a skillful game, famously played by Sir Francis Drake in 1588!

I-SPY points: 20

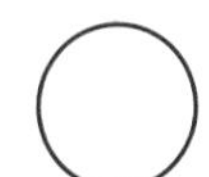

Date: ____________

UNICYCLE

Have fun on a one-wheel unicycle...

I-SPY points: 30

Date: ____________

TANDEM

...or on a bicycle made for two!

I-SPY points: 20

Date: ____________

WHITE CLIFFS

Take a stroll at the seaside, from the chalky white cliffs...

I-SPY points: 20

Date: ____________

PIER

...to the end of the pier.

I-SPY points: 15

Date: ____________

LIGHTHOUSE

Perhaps you can climb to the top of the lighthouse...

I-SPY points: 15

Date: ____________

HARBOUR

...or take a boat trip?

I-SPY points: 15

Date: ____________

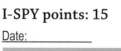

SAIL BOATS

Beginners learn to sail in small dinghies.

I-SPY points: 5

Date: ____________

NARROW BOAT

Go for a stroll along a canal to see some colourful barges and long boats.

I-SPY points: 5

Date: ____________

FORTH RAIL BRIDGE

Up to 200 trains a day cross the Forth Bridge every day in Scotland.

I-SPY points: 20

Date: ____________

I-SPY points: 5 points for any other major road or rail bridge

STARLING

Cheeky birds which gather at motorway service stations as they watch out for titbits from passing motorists.

I-SPY points: 5

Date:

BLACK-HEADED GULL

Flocks of gulls are often seen following the farmer's plough or at landfill sites.

I-SPY points: 5

Date:

MAGPIE

A large black-and-white bird with long tail. You will often see them feeding on road kill.

I-SPY points: 5

Date:

ROOK

Flocks of these distinctive large crows can often be seen feeding in roadside fields.

I-SPY points: 5

Date:

PHEASANT

Most often spotted strutting around verges and field boundaries. The males are more colourful than the females.

I-SPY points: 10

Date: ____________

HOUSE SPARROW

Can be seen dust bathing at the side of the road or scavenging for crumbs under tables at roadside pubs.

I-SPY points: 5

Date: ____________

BUZZARD

Buzzards are very large and can regularly be spotted from the car, circling in the sky or sitting on fence posts.

I-SPY points: 10

Date: ____________

PIED WAGTAIL

Wagtails happily swap from countryside to urban life and back. They're as happy in the motorway services as in rivers and streams.

I-SPY points: 5

Date: ____________

COMMON YEW

You are most likely to find yew trees growing in churchyards.

I-SPY points: 5

Date: ____________

COMMON ASH

Ash is used to make hammer and spade handles and is also popular with furniture makers.

I-SPY points: 5

Date: ____________

BEECH

Easily found in spring: bluebells carpet their wizened roots.

I-SPY points: 5

Date: ____________

HORSE CHESTNUT

Best known for their autumn crop of nuts which children can use to play "conkers" for hours.

I-SPY points: 5

Date: ____________

HAWTHORN

Commonly found as an impenetrable thorny hedge, ideal for containing animals.

I-SPY points: 5

Date: ____________

ELDER

The elder is small by tree standards, usually not much more than a bush.

I-SPY points: 5

Date: ____________

BLACKTHORN

The fruit of the blackthorn is a small bitter plum or "sloe", often used to make a tasty jam or sloe gin.

I-SPY points: 5

Date: ____________

SILVER BIRCH

Long associated with the start of new life due to its outstanding ability to colonise bare land after a forest is felled.

I-SPY points: 5

Date: ____________

VINTAGE AEROPLANE

This biplane has two wings, two seats and a propeller.

I-SPY points: 20

Date: ____________

AIRSHIPS OR BLIMPS

Often used for advertising.

I-SPY points: 20

Date: ____________

MICROLITE AIRCRAFT

Microlight aircraft fly at around 100km/h (60mph), and as high as 1,500m (5,000ft) – any higher and it's too cold!

I-SPY points: 20

Date: ____________

HOT AIR BALLOON

Hot air balloons can often be seen hovering over the countryside on warm days.

I-SPY points: 20

Date: ____________

PLANE TAKING OFF

You will see planes taking off every couple of minutes from a busy airport.

I-SPY points: 20

Date:

GLIDER

Gliders are often towed into the sky by more powerful planes. They have no engine and use the wind and hot air to fly.

I-SPY points: 20

Date:

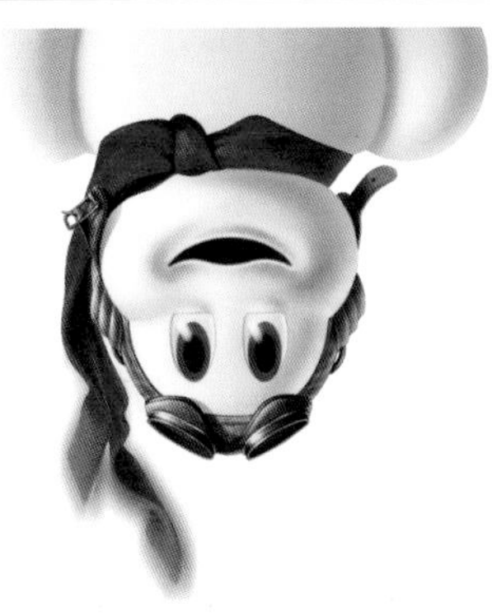

SKYDIVER

Experienced skydivers are able to land on a handkerchief!

I-SPY points: 20

Date:

Over the Tracks

LEVEL CROSSING

Stop at the level crossing to watch the train go by. Always be careful at level crossings.

I-SPY points: 5

Date: ____________

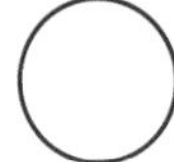

STEAM TRAIN

If you are lucky, you'll see an old steam train – just like the Hogwarts Express. Look for the steam coming out of the chimney.

I-SPY points: 5

Date: ____________

FOOTBRIDGE

Stand on a footbridge and feel trains whiz past beneath your feet! Hold on to your hat!

I-SPY points: 5

Date: ____________

WEIR

Weirs regulate the flow of water along a river.

I-SPY points: 20

Date:

CANAL LOCK

Locks on canals change the level of the water. Watch what happens as the lock fills with water and the boat in the lock rises up!

I-SPY points: 20

Date:

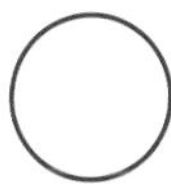

RAIL AND ROAD BRIDGE

The new road bridge in the background runs parallel to the old railway bridge.

I-SPY points: 10

Date:

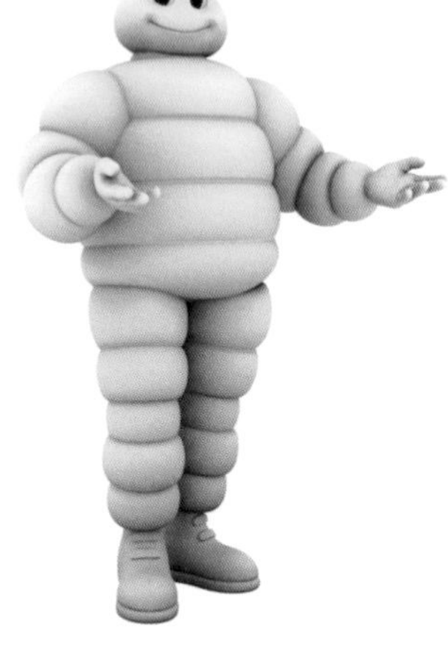

SUSPENSION BRIDGE

The Clifton Suspension Bridge in Bristol spans the River Avon, 75 m (245 ft) below. It was designed by the famous Victorian engineer I.K. Brunel (1806 – 1859).

I-SPY points: 20

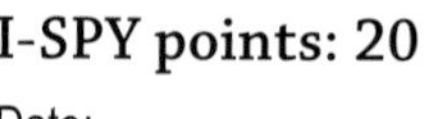

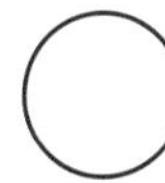

20MPH SPEED LIMIT

Usually by schools.

I-SPY points: 5

Date: ____________

CYCLE LANE

I-SPY points: 5

Date: ____________

KEEP CLEAR

I-SPY points: 5

Date: ____________

SLOW

I-SPY points: 5

Double if you can spot a dual language sign

Date: ____________

Road Signs

Watch out for these animal-related signs particularly in roads passing through the countryside.

I-SPY points: 15 for each of these

FROGS

Date: ____________

HORSES

Date: ____________

SHEEP

Date: ____________

DEER

Date: ____________

SQUIRRELS

Date: ____________

DUCKS

Date: ____________

UNEVEN ROAD

I-SPY points: 10

Date: ____________

ROUNDABOUT

I-SPY points: 10

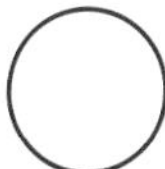

Date: ____________

ONE WAY

I-SPY points: 10

Date: ____________

NATIONAL SPEED

Maximum 70mph.

I-SPY points: 10

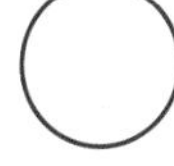

Date: ____________

I-SPY points: 10 for each of these

NEW LAYOUT

Date:

ICE WARNING

Date:

TRACTORS TURNING

Date:

LEVEL CROSSING

Date:

CHILDREN CROSSING

Date:

ELDERLY PEOPLE

Date:

BLIND SUMMIT

I-SPY points: 10

Date:

CONGESTION ZONE

I-SPY points: 5

Date:

BROWN ROAD SIGN

I-SPY points: 5

Date:

MOTORWAY SIGN

I-SPY points: 5

Date:

20 SPEED LIMIT

I-SPY points: 5

Date: ____________

30 SPEED LIMIT

I-SPY points: 5

Date: ____________

40 SPEED LIMIT

I-SPY points: 5

Date: ____________

50 SPEED LIMIT

I-SPY points: 5

Date: ____________

)LD FASHIONED ROAD SIGN

)ld signs not only point you in the ight direction, but the circular top ells you which district you're in!

-SPY points: 10

)ate: ____________

ANCIENT ROAD SIGN

Before the 19th century, milestones let travellers know how far they had to walk or ride to their destination.

I-SPY points: 10

Date: ____________

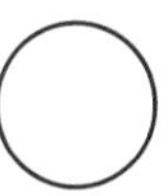

STATELY HOME

Chatsworth House in Derbyshire is the home of the Dukes of Devonshire.

I-SPY points: 15

Double if it is open to the public

Date:

WATER TOWER

This brick water tower is topped by fancy crenellations.

I-SPY points: 15

Date:

TUDOR HOUSE

Black beams and white walls were common on 16th- and 17th-century houses.

I-SPY points: 15

Date:

OAST HOUSES

These were originally built as drying kilns for hops and malt. Mostly found in Kent.

I-SPY points: 15

Date: ____________

DERELICT HOUSES

If you fancy something a little more comfortable, move on from this tumbledown house, to the grand entrance to a stately home.

I-SPY points: 15

Date: ____________

STATELY HOME ENTRANCE

I-SPY points: 15

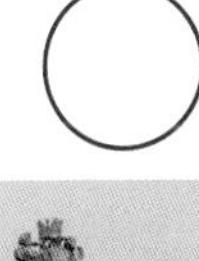

Date: ____________

CASTLE RUINS

Some castles have crumbled over the years, while others have been well looked-after.

I-SPY points: 10

Date: ____________

CASTLE

I-SPY points: 10

Date: ____________

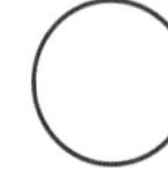

VIADUCT

Viaducts carry roads and rail across gorges. Look how many bricks were used to built this one!

I-SPY points: 25

Date: ____________

Fuel for the Journey

There are many different companies supplying petrol and diesel to the millions of Britain's motorists. Garages are decorated in company colours and emblazoned with oil company's signs. Some also have supermarkets in them.

I-SPY points: 5 for each of these

ESSO

Date: ____________

BP

Date: ____________

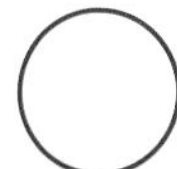

Fuel for the Journey

I-SPY points: 5 for each of these, 5 points for any other petrol sign

TEXACO

Date: ____________

MURCO

Date: ____________

SHELL

Date: ____________

TOTAL

Date: ____________

Places of worship are always worth looking at. You will find them in a number of styles, from ancient ruined buildings to modern structures that look quite unlike one another.

CHURCH

I-SPY points: 10

Date: ____________

MOSQUE

I-SPY points: 10

Date: ____________

I-SPY points: 10

Date: ____________

MODERN CHURCH

ABBEY

Coloured light pours in through beautiful stained glass windows.

I-SPY points: 10

Date: ____________

CATHEDRAL

Many cathedrals are decorated with amazing carved stone figures

I-SPY points: 10

Date: ____________

RUINED ABBEY

This abbey is now just a skeletal, roofless shell, but still interesting.

I-SPY points: 15

Date: ____________

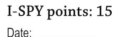

Keeping Time

Many cities and towns have public clocks, as do churches and even some farms. Here are some to keep you ticking over.

SUNDIAL

I-SPY points: 10

Date: ____________

CHURCH CLOCK

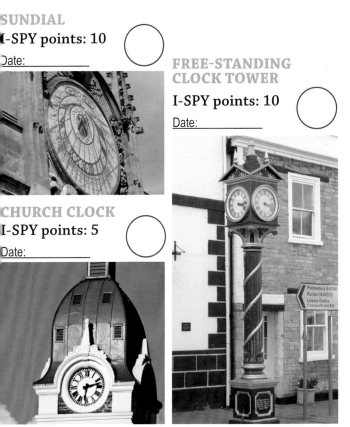

I-SPY points: 5

Date: ____________

FREE-STANDING CLOCK TOWER

I-SPY points: 10

Date: ____________

STATION CLOCK

I-SPY points: 5

Date: ____________

CLOCK ON SIDE OF BUILDING

I-SPY points: 10

Date: ____________

MODERN CITY CLOCK

I-SPY points: 10

Date: ____________

AIRPORT

You may be continuing your journey by 'plane...

I-SPY points: 10

Date: ____________

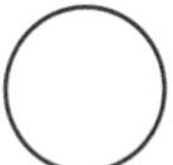

TRAIN STATION

...or you may be catching a train.

I-SPY points: 10

Date: ____________

CAMPSITE

Perhaps your car journey may end at a campsite. Enjoy your holiday!

I-SPY points: 10

Date: __________

SEASIDE

...or you may have some fun at the seaside. Don't forget your bucket and spade!

I-SPY points: 10

Date: __________

Index

First published by Michelin Maps and Guides 2009

Created and produced by Blue Sky Publishing Limited.

Print services by FingerPrint International Book production - fingerprint@pandora.be
The publisher gratefully acknowledges the contribution of the I-Spy team: Camilla Lovell, Ruth Neilson, Judith Millidge and Faron Watts in the production of this title. The publisher gratefully acknowledges the contribution of Anthony Dixon, David Whistlecraft, Mark Bicknell, Britain on View, Thames Valley Police, Truck & Driver Magazine, David Fenwick and Unitaw Limited who provided the photographs in this book. Other images in the public domain and used under a creative commons licence. The publishers are grateful for the kind assistance and reproduction rights granted by all the companies and agencies illustrated within this I-Spy book.

Reprinted 2012 16 15 14 13 12 11 10 9 8

HOW TO GET YOUR I-SPY CERTIFICATE AND BADGE

Every time you score 1000 points or more in an I-Spy book, you can apply for a certificate

Here's what to do, step by step:

Certificate

- Ask an adult to check your score
- Ask his or her permission to apply for a certificate
- Apply online to www.ispymichelin.com
- Enter your name and address and the completed title
- We will send you back via e mail your certificate for the title

Badge

- Each I-Spy title has a cut out (page corner) token at the back of the book
- Collect five tokens from different I-Spy titles
- Put Second Class Stamps on two strong envelopes
- Write your own address on one envelope and put a £1 coin inside it (for protection). Fold, but do not seal the envelope, and place it inside the second envelope
- Write the following address on the second envelope, seal it carefully and post to:

I-Spy Books
Michelin Maps and Guides
Hannay House
39 Clarendon Road
Watford
WD17 1JA